redcedar
REVIEW

2012

Red Cedar Review (ISSN 0034-1967) is an annual literary magazine published in the spring by Michigan State University undergraduates in collaboration with Michigan State University Press with support from the Michigan State University College of Arts and Letters and Department of English.

BUSINESS OFFICE

Subscriptions, orders, renewals, change of address, claims for missing issues: Michigan State University Press Jouranls; PO Box 121; Congers, NY 10920-0121; TEL (845) 267-3054; FAX (845) 267-3478; EMAIL *msupjournals@cambeywest. com*. *All other inquiries*: Michigan State University Press Journals, 1405 S. Harrison Rd.; Ste. 25; East Lansing, MI 48823-5245; TEL (517) 884-6917; FAX (517) 432-2611; EMAIL *journals@msu.edu*; WEB *www.msupress.msu.edu/ journals/rcr.*

FOR MORE INFORMATION

For more information, visit the Red Cedar Review website at www.msupress.msu.edu/journals/rcr/. **Please do not send manuscripts to MSU Press.**

	1 YEAR
U.S. Individual	$18
International Individual	$28
U.S. Institution	$36
International Institution	$46
Student	$11

plus shipping and handling*

VIA USPS. * Shipping and handling for each copy: DOMESTIC: $6.00; INTERNATIONAL: $8.00. For airmail, contact *msupjournals@cambeywest.com* for quote before ordering.

Prepayment required: check, money order, Visa, MasterCard accepted. Payment must be in U.S. currency drawn from a U.S. bank.

RETURN, CREDIT, REFUND & CLAIM POLICY

Returns are not accepted. MSU Press Journals Division can provide full or partial credit only for subscription orders. Credits issued for cancellations will be pro-rated. Credit can be transferred only to other MSU Press journals, not to MSU Press book products. Pending subscriptions can be refunded in full. Allow 8-12 weeks for processing. Domestic claims must be received within 3 months of publication date. International claims must be received within 6 months of publication date.

Red Cedar Review is indexed in Current Abstracts, Humanities International Complete, Humanities International Index, Literature Online (LION), Literary Reference Center, ProQuest, Scopus, and Ulrichsweb.

Red Cedar Review participates in Project MUSE*, a Johns Hopkins University initiative that provides online institutional access to leading scholarly publications in the arts, humanities, and social sciences at *http://muse.jhu.edu.*

Michigan State University Press is a member of the Green Press Initiative and is committed to developing and encouraging ecologically responsible publishing practices. For more information about the Green Press Initiative and the use of recycled paper in book publishing, please visit *www.greenpressinitiative.org*

You are invited to join the

FRIENDS OF THE
redcedar
REVIEW

Please consider becoming a patron of Red Cedar Review. For the past 47 years, we have been committed to exploring all genres, by publishing both emerging and established writers. Your generous support will help us continue our mission of promoting excellent writing and providing a forum for creativity within the student literary community. Your tax-deductible contribution* can be made by check or credit card, and unless you wish to remain annonymous you will be gratefully acknowledged in the journal and with a letter of receipt.

FRIENDS OF THE WRITTEN WORD

☐ POETRY SECTION SPONSOR..............................$300 *(includes one-year subscription)*
☐ FICTION SECTION SPONSOR..............................$300 *(includes one-year subscription)*
☐ INTERVIEW SECTION SPONSOR........................$500 *(includes one-year subscription + 1 guest subscription)*
☐ ART & GRAPHICS SECTION SPONSOR .... $600 *(includes one-year subscription + 1 guest subscription)*
☐ VOLUME SPONSOR (ANNUAL ISSUE)................$1,000 *(includes one-year subscription + 2 guest subscriptions)*

FRIENDS OF THE SPOKEN WORD

Your gift will support a variety of literary events on campus, including readings and visits from guest authors. Visiting writers have included essayist Tom Lynch and poet Diane Glancy.

☐ POETRY SECTION SPONSOR..............................$300 *(includes one-year subscription)*
☐ FICTION SECTION SPONSOR..............................$300 *(includes one-year subscription)*
☐ INTERVIEW SECTION SPONSOR........................$500 *(includes one-year subscription + 1 guest subscription)*
☐ ART & GRAPHICS SECTION SPONSOR .... $600 *(includes one-year subscription + 1 guest subscription)*
☐ VOLUME SPONSOR (ANNUAL ISSUE)................$1,000 *(includes one-year subscription + 2 guest subscriptions)*

GIFTS

Please complete this form, make checks payable to *Michigan State University*, specify *Red Cedar Review* on the memo line, and send to: Michgan State University Press, Journal Division; 1405 S. Harrison Rd., Ste. 25; East Lansing, MI 48823-5245. To charge your credit card, fax the complete form to (517)353-6766.

☐ I WISH TO REMAIN ANONYMOUS

NAME (PLEASE PRINT)

STREET ADDRESS

CITY/STATE/ZIP

E-MAIL ADDRESS

☐ Visa
☐ Mastercard

ACCOUNT NUMBER   **EXPIRATION DATE**

* Contributions to Michigan State University Press are tax-deductible. However, according to IRS guidelines, the value of any goods/services (subscriptions) received in connection with your gift must be deducted from the gross amount of your contribution to determine the amount eligible for tax advantages and employer matching gift programs.

Thank you for your generous support of this exceptional publication!

RCR 47 STAFF

RCR 47 EDITING STAFF

From left to right: (front row) Sarah Sherman, Arts Editor; Becca Pierce, Assistant Prose Editor; Amelia Larson, Managing Edior; Shelby Dosser, Assistant Managing Editor; Kaitlyn Canary, Assistant Poetry Editor; (back row) Korey Hurni, Poetry Editor; Alex Henderson, Prose Editor

Opposite page
Row 1 (from left to right): Shelby Dosser, Sarah Sherman, Kelsey Kaptur, Michelle Hevelhorst
Row 2 (from left to right): Katie Conley, Korey Hurni, Kien Lam, Alejandra Ortega
Row 3 (from left to right): Becca Pierce, Amelia Larson, Alexandra Ghaly, Alex Henderson
Row 4 (from left to right): Sarah Valicevic, Michael Kulick, Nicholas Yodock, Kaitlyn Canary
Row 5 (from left to right): Vikram Mandelia, Jamie Hardy, Austin Vankirk

Staff members not pictured: Ashley Madau, Susan Weber, Brianne Ross, Justin Cook, Kelsey Beachum, Kate Sheka

CONTENTS

EDITOR'S NOTE

AMELIA LARSON

It is both a pity and a blessing that many staff positions of the Red Cedar Review, particularly the senior editing positions, are transitory from year to year. Rarely does any senior staff member stay in their position as prose or poetry or managing editor for more than two consecutive years, if that. When your entire staff is comprised of college undergraduates who are constantly moving on to new platforms of life, this is inevitable; it's just too bad that most managing editors only get to oversee one issue of the journal before having to entrust to someone else the welfare of what has essentially become his or her "baby." Change, however, is ultimately a good thing. I believe the Red Cedar Review would not have had as long and diverse a life as it has without a continual flux of voices and opinions. We should strive not to replicate the past, but to simultaneously preserve and transcend it; it was in this spirit that the issue you hold in your hands was created.

To my knowledge, this is the first issue in the history of the Red Cedar Review to exclusively publish college undergraduate contributors. This is a radical departure from the journal's past, in which everyone from professional working authors to prison inmates have sent in their work for review; and, truly, this has contributed greatly to the journal's rich history. It was thanks to this broad method that the Red Cedar Review has had the privilege of publishing works by famously talented writers such as Pablo Neruda, Jim Harrison, and Margaret Atwood, to name only a few. The decision this year to accept submissions exclusively from college undergrads across the country raised more than a few eyebrows, to say the least. This issue also marks the first edition of the journal to intentionally include the genre of visual art alongside literature. Photography and other select artwork has always had a scattered, here-and-there sort of presence in the Red Cedar Review, but this year we have finally made it official, sending out submission calls for all types of undergraduate-produced art and recruiting a jury of MSU art students to review them.

Many of us on the staff, myself included, had moments of serious doubt that the journal could be produced using only undergraduate submissions. The artistic and literary youth of America, no matter how creative, diverse, and enthusiastic they may be, are—let's face it—more prone to bad writing and bad art than the older generations of greater experience. As an aspiring artist and writer myself, I may say this with personal certainty. We are prone to typos and grammatical errors. We are prone to certain traps and dead ends of narrative and certain clichés in poetry. We are prone to make paintings and take photographs that seem to be missing something. And really, on a general level, it only makes sense. We are young, we are still learning. We have only recently found our artistic and literary feet to stand on— it will be some time before we are able to run without ever stumbling. Why, then, did the Red Cedar Review make such an effort in this issue to publish only young writers and artists who are still getting used to their feet?

It is because, as apt as many young creators may be to make formal mistakes, they are also the first ones to look to when you want to find new life and inspiration in art.

The pulse of a generation is visible in these pages. From poem to prose to painting and photograph, we see the vibrant, burgeoning expression of evolving artists and writers across the country, the young men and women who will go on to become the Nerudas and Harrisons and Atwoods of tomorrow. Last year, as the Red Cedar Review celebrated its 47th anniversary, we took a long, retrospective look back on our decades of rich history. This year, we went looking for a new future in art and literature, a new youth and revitalization, and we found it.

It has been my pleasure and privilege to work with many talented and dedicated lovers of art and literature in putting this issue together. I am thankful to all of them, especially to my assistant managing editor, Shelby, who understands that anything worth doing is worth laughing about, and to my editing staff, none of whom ever pulled even a single punch in the creation of this issue. I am also grateful to our supportive advisors in the English department, Robin Silbergleid and Steve Arch, to Chris Corneal who supervised the redesign of the journal, and to Margot Kielhorn and Teal Amthor-Shaffer of the MSU Press, all of whom have played key roles in the production and success of this journal.

I cannot say for sure whether the decision to publish undergraduates only will survive beyond my one year of managing the Red Cedar Review, but I am certain of this; as long as there are young innovators stumbling along on new feet, they will find a place to stand. It is my hope that the Red Cedar Review might continue to act as that standing place for as long as writers and artists have need of it.

TO MY FUTURE OFFSPRING

LEENA JOSHI

I thought
about teaching you
what death is, or more likely, you
finding out and asking me why, how, where
we go then. I'm suddenly terrified of this even though
you don't yet exist in any sense. Right now I am keeping grief
in small, manageable packets. I am quietly bewildered
by potatoes I've forgotten, inspecting the sprouts
in their eyes, feeling slightly foolish for not
using them earlier. Right now grief
is easily quelled: I take a knife
to the growth, and life
stays simple.

THE VERDICT: BEAUTY FIRST WITHOUT BLAME.

ERIK JAMES WILBUR

Yesterday I saw you true
from a barstool,
to the taste of oak & dull gasoline
chased with sweet, stale middle-America.

Four lonely lamps
spaced   evenly   over   rosewood
hung like geese on meat hooks,
and glowed like ripe pomegranates still dressed in morning rain.

With clemency,
they whispered pallid light through
shackled eyes.

In a nervous glass,
brazen bits of carbon slipped
up & out
with vulgar grace.

And I recalled you,
truly
better in your Sunday best:
a pistol-grip-ivory blouse, an olive (branch) a-line skirt,
the color of flickering candlelight held up & back by a peacock brooch,
the color of October, 1886,
the color of leaves in Leviticus.
A semblance of a specter in lace and linen,

You must have been somewhere fast asleep.

TO MR. & MRS. TEMPE

JARED SHAFFER

Passing through the outskirts of Tempe today, I decide to spend the night with Anna. She opens her door wearing only a *Top Gun* tee-shirt and a pair of high-heeled flip-flops. I appreciate her transparency.

Later that night, I am sitting with my back against the foot of her bed while she lies above me, running her fingers through my hair. I wish I could hear everything she says twice: as soon as she says it and then an echo of her voice bouncing off the wood paneling in front of us. She always speaks as though she were a new planet forming, ideas colliding randomly like huge asteroids hurtling towards one another in space.

"I think God has given up on us. He saw the violence, the discrimination, the overall indecency, and he said, 'Forget it, I'm going to Mercury!'"

"Not to mention he kicked us out of Eden over an apple," I say.

"Now as for Jesus, that's who we could really use. I mean he cared enough to die and then come back. What a madman, but we need that."

"It's too bad. He's probably stuck on Mercury."

Grabbing the beer bottle out of my hand, she stands up on the bed, balancing herself on one leg. She hurls the bottle at the wall and giggles as the glass rains down on the carpet.

"Who is going to clean that up?" she asks. "Who the heck is going to clean that up?"

I stare at Tom Cruise's motionless and crumpled face on the floor. He is smiling and giving me a thumbs-up.

She begs to come with me on the interstate the next morning, pushing her breasts up against my chest as relentlessly as grandmothers force sweets into the hands of their departing families.

"I have a wife Anna," I tell her.

She motions to her bed like a magician revealing that his female assistant has not, in fact, been chopped in half.

"That's different. When I get back on the highway my life becomes my job again, a job I do to feed my family. To bring you along, well I feel like it would be breaking some sort of unwritten rule."

"Family, wife, job, job, family, wife," she says. "Didn't you understand me last night? The world is ending soon. You're going to miss me when the road splits in half and swallows you and that truck. Or when the clouds turn vertically and start to come after you like tornados. Damn that'll be fun, and I bet you won't be thinking about the time your wife brought home new throw pillows."

Now her feet are dangling out of the truck's window, and her head rests in my lap. Every time I switch gears the truck hiccups, sliding her Aviators down the bridge of her nose. On deserted four-lane stretches I spin the wheel like we are on an old pirate ship in the midst of a hurricane. She tumbles from the leather seat and lies sprawled out on the cabin floor, pretending to be dead.

"Oh no, I hate to kill another one this way."

"It's worse than you think," she says. "I'm paralyzed from the neck down."

"So you can talk, but we can't have sex?"

She climbs back into the seat and gently slaps my cheek.

"What are you hauling in this bad boy anyway?"

"Honey."

"Honey?"

"Over two tons back there."

"Don't you know a honey wagon is the name for the trucks that empty Port-a-Johns?"

"This is actual honey though——"

"Which *means*, we are transporting over two tons of shit from Arizona to Oregon." She makes the shape of a circle with her fingertips and then pushes them apart, raising her eyebrows while mouthing the word *boom*.

Somewhere in Nevada we are pouring honey into each other's mouths. It's a gas station just north of Reno that's also a Taco Bell, that's also a 24-hour Laundromat. We are sitting on the pull-out lift of the trailer. I have already lost two bear-shaped bottles of honey to her, payment for my incorrect guesses to her riddle: What food never goes bad?

"What's your wife's name?" Anna says. "Wait, stop. Don't tell me. Does she look like me?"

"I don't think she looks like you."

"And when we're together, do you think about her?"

"You sound like a wife. Do I ask you about any of the others?"

"Let's go to the coast before Oregon. There is something about the salt water that helps me tan."

"Do they take you out on the highway too?"

"Maybe we can visit San Francisco. You think we could dive off the Golden Gate Bridge and survive the fall?"

"Clearly they take you to better places than Oregon," I say. "Do you give it up more often because of that?"

The eyes of the bear she is holding bulge, filling with honey. "Bring me back to Tempe," she says, staring at me without blinking, the same stare she wears when she argues with her mother on the phone. It's the face that means *For the last time, I won't be home for Christmas this year* and *Seriously, bring me back to Tempe.*

"Come on Anna, I have a schedule. You know how this all works."

"Tell your boss not to worry, honey never spoils."

Though drivers are taught to ignore hitchhikers, I pick up Amir and Joe because it doesn't feel right to hurtle by a father and his young son going eighty miles per hour on an empty two-lane highway in Nevada. Especially when the two are covered in dirt, and especially when the father sticks his thumb out so far into the road that a passing car could easily clip his nail with its side view mirror. But more than anything, it is Anna grabbing and squeezing my hand as we approach the pair, after four hours without so much as a throat clearing, that causes me to pull over and offer my services.

They are both wearing thin white robes caked in red clay. Neither one has shoes. Joe could not be more than ten years old and though he is half his father's height, he already has a thin imitation of Amir's mustache and his hands are so big that he can probably palm a basketball. Amir carries their only luggage, a faded leather satchel with a short handle and a longer strap.

"Where are you headed?" I ask as they settle into the back seat.

"As far south as you and your wife are going," Amir says. He seems satisfied with this brevity, but Joe is not.

"We are seeking warmer climates," Joe says. In the rearview I see him cross his arms and turn to the window, daring his chauffeurs to ask questions with his apparent indifference.

"And why on earth are you after those?" Anna asks, her hand still wrapped around mine.

First looking to his father for approval (a nod and smile from Amir), Joe pulls out a plastic bag from his pocket. In it are three light green seeds that resemble pistachios.

"These are seeds from the tallest tree that ever grew. Once we find the right climates, Dad and I will plant them and wait one full week for the new tallest tree to grow. Its leaves will be the size of battleships and its roots will be mountains all on their own. We'll climb to the very top too and—"

"Be able to kiss the hand of God," Amir says. He smiles at Joe, but I can't tell whether he is proud of his son's imagination or of his certainty.

"How did you get hold of these fantastic seeds?" Anna says.

"Well it's obvious isn't it?" Joe says, uncrossing his left arm and raising it with an air of authority that only children and zealots own. "We made it to the top of the first tree and God gave them to us."

Once more, Amir smiles. He blows into Joe's ear and Joe is just a child again, giggling and covering his ear with one of those gigantic hands. His teeth, little sugar cubes, look like they have been thrust into his gums from random angles.

We reach the outskirts of Tempe that night, and Anna insists that Amir and Joe stay the night at her house. She moves about the house in a frenzied state I have never before seen, apologizing for the dusty television, the uncomfortable pull-out bed with the ugly floral pattern, the unscented candles, the hand soap that smells too feminine . . . all of this, to two visitors who leave mud stains wherever they sit and have yellow blotches beneath their arms.

Refusing my Chinese take-out proposal, she fries salmon she found lurking in the back of the freezer, coupling it with a side of microwavable biscuits. She drenches both with the bear honey.

"Truly, this house deserves children," Amir says after dinner. Joe has fallen asleep on the pull-out with his hands stuck in the prayer position, a result of his drowsiness as well as the honey.

I take a long sip of my beer, but Anna says, "It's surprising how often my husband's job keeps him away from home."

"I wish Joe had this constancy though." Amir pauses as he looks down at his son, and the same grin reappears. "But of course, out of necessity, that is not possible."

"Then change for a final time Amir. Find a job here and settle down, stop traveling," I say.

"But there are many more trees to be planted. Joe and I have accepted our reality. If we quit, who then will take up the task? Surely you all cannot, for what good will come from disrupting another young family? This household must flourish."

I receive a letter today with a return address but no name. Though I have not seen or spoken with Anna in over a year, I still only know one person who lives in Tempe that uses neon green ink and puts circles above her "i's" instead of dots. Inside the envelope, there is a sticky note with the familiar handwriting attached to a folded letter as well as a tiny plastic bag that contains one of Amir and Joe's seeds. Anna writes:

> *I ate one, I think you should too.*
> *P.S. I kept the pacifier, did not want to use two stamps.*

Unfolding the other piece of paper reveals a note written with black-colored pencil, its words some mix of cursive and print:

> *Dear Mr. & Mrs. Tempe,*
>
> *Joe and I are in Peru. If you can believe it, monkeys are the squirrel equivalent here. We are planting, growing and gathering more seeds every day. We will block out the sun if that's what it takes for every man, woman and child to be able to touch God.*
>
> *I hope you took my advice. I imagine that the baby would be a few months old by now, and an extra pacifier never did any harm. Also the two seeds- they won't grow in Tempe, but Joe demanded that I include them. He may be entering the mysterious and dark throes of puberty, where what he wishes was real governs his actions instead of what is real. This is what you all may look forward to. Yet, our mission guides him to reason.*
>
> *Pining for honeyed salmon,*
> *Amir*

I pocket the letter and place the seed on my tongue. In spite of what Amir writes, perhaps the seed will germinate in my stomach. Its roots will spread throughout my body, overtaking my blood vessels and nerve endings until the trunk bursts from my mouth, climbing toward a wide-open heaven.

YOUNG LOVIN

LEENA JOSHI

toothy and
circling grin,
doo wop and
thumb war—all that
won't turn
old

it clicks
from no doubt your
forthcoming and not
giving a lick—my attraction to
that form of living

I lull the run from
and
ah, allow it to root

now goddamn body furorz
lip trailing limb
tracing path and birthmark;
a murmur into your collar bowl

willow into
our air mingling
ligand of atom,
amygdala imprint
marking a pillow
with fair moan

okay culmination
(right? can't fight it)
unravel how a map would drift
from a high window

now fold all
into our dural gray
of cranial—it will hold
the lot of
our hot gradation—
it was callow,
but radiant

IF I WERE TO LIE IN LIMBO

KEITH MAGNUSON

Staring, staring as the ash burns lower and lower to the knuckles, and then I smell the burning cigarette filter; a concluding, half-conscious drag. I lift the corner of the bed and grind my remains beneath the bedpost. I don't want to be out in the main lobby this early in the morning. I'm the only patient awake and there's only one person out there, keeping watch and judging me. I've had to use the bathroom in the small hours of the night once, my toes cold against the tile as I rushed across it. I had felt the stare. It pinned me down—a girl, naked on the table—and his scalpel-glare cut into me through the bathroom walls. It had despised me for being a smoker, being awake, being here, for being the reason that he sat through the night at a desk in the dark; I've never gone out at night after that.

I want other patients to be walking around, the ones who actually become lost in their thoughts, their realities until you can see right through their frames. Those are the ones you don't have to worry about. They consume the stares of anybody around to take the judgment, but that doesn't matter to them. Their world is in their heads.

Streams of sunlight are just now reaching the tips of my toes, making them glow and warming them as the rising sun peaks over the horizon at me. It's a good feeling, but my window only enables this for a brief minute before the rays angle downwards once again.

It's been seasons since I've last seen him. They don't allow him to visit me in the ward and I had only agreed to stay, confined away, until he had a plan to get me out. But the letter had arrived just a few days prior. He would be here today and we would leave this place. I hope that everyone looks up as we walk out. I will walk with him defiantly and they will wish they were me. They'll see him smile with genuine happiness, the way his blond hair curls atop his head, and his perfect composure and confidence. He will control the room, and they will see that he's smiling for me.

The nurse is making her rounds and her heels clack across the tile in the hallway. The sound dies away as she enters each room to deliver the medications. In the past month, I've learned how to cradle the pills under my tongue, to pocket them at the very back as I drink the water that she places in front of me. The clack of her heels swells and alerts me and she's nearly at my door as I try to seem asleep. She nudges me until I sit up and she directs me to take the pills. She watches me with suspicion; she remembers what I was like when I got here. I had put the pills through a hole in my mattress. She discovered it and they changed my room. To her, I am merely a stubborn mouth that she must force pills down. But they rest beneath my tongue as she talks with me and I persist under her gazing eyes—two skeptics that can only disbelieve me. She scans the bed and under it before she is satisfied. She continues down the hall, her heels punching out their clacks as she enters the next room.

The dissolving pills become bitter and sickening and I let the taste pool up as I walk to the bathroom. I turn a faucet and the medicated saliva mixes with water on its way down the drain. I look up and into the mirror. The mirror helps me brush my teeth and I thank the reflection for meticulously rendering my movements.

"Thanks."

I notice that my black hair needs nurturing. A smile's in there too, though. Fuck the hair; people want to see me smile. I've always pictured myself with blond hair anyway. In the dark, before this place, I would stand in front of the mirror in the dark and pretend it was. I would say, "My hair is blond," and look into the mirror and it would never show me any proof that I was wrong. Black hair doesn't compliment the color of my eyes, a pale blue that begs for blond hair.

Yet staring back at me are brown eyes and I turn away in disbelief, avoiding the reflection. How can a mirror be wrong? I double-check, inching closer, closer to the image and the brown. The dark hue wreaks havoc on my complexion. Every feature on my face is plain, is dulled by the play of black and brown—colors I know never to place together, that God wouldn't place together.

"What happened to my eyes?" I lament.

"What a weird question. They're where they've always been," says a voice from behind. I glance over and behind me with the mirror. He is standing there. I wheel around to face him.

"I knew you'd find a way! I got your letter. I read it every night before I go to sleep." I'm in his arms before he can respond.

"With the surprise on your face just now I was beginning to have doubts."

"You're here pretty early, though. How nice of you," I say with a coy smile. "They still haven't served breakfast yet."

"What was that about your eyes?"

"The light must have played tricks on me. I was brushing my teeth and I swore they were brown."

"Let me take a look." He holds me gently below the shoulders, crouching to my eye level.

"They look blue to me. Don't worry. They're waiting for me back at the desk. I told them I personally wanted to fetch you, even from the bathroom," he says jokingly. "Let's get out of here. It's been forever since we've been to our pond."

"I would love that," I reply. "I'll be right out." He walks out and I wash my face. I keep my eyes from checking in the mirror one more time. I trust him, and I follow him.

The autumn air feels good on my skin. The clouds all hold a wispy quality to them, like they had been pulled to the breaking point and yet refuse to tear. The sun's rays are just beginning to cut through the distant tree-line, bending and reflecting off the nearby pond and creating a steaming vapor.

"The pond looks like a giant bowl of soup," he says, his coat pulled tightly about him. I picked it out for him, a trench coat that stretched down to the mid-thigh, covering his square shoulders in black. I can't remember where I got it; it looks good on him.

"The pond looks like the sky, except that it's upside down and raining. You and I are walking on the sky right now, but how could we ever tell?" Both are true but the pond will look like something new every day. That's what I love about these walks.

"I'm sure it would become fairly obvious once we started plummeting to Earth," he says. He pushes me with his shoulder slightly, playfully. His composure changes rapidly, his smile falling and fixing on a somber expression that I've seen him use before. "Listen, now that we're finally out of the ward, I've been meaning to tell you something."

I listen for him to continue, but I hear the swelling clack of the nurse's footsteps from farther up the path. I quickly jog off the trail and away from him, as if transfixed on an object submerged just off the pond's shoreline. He stands motionless on the path, waiting for her to pass him by. I urge him to keep walking, flailing my arms and mouthing mute sounds to him but he remains stolid, immobile. She passes him without a word. I plan on giving him hell.

"I thought we talked about this," I said. I try not to look into his eyes, which are showing signs of annoyance that spill out and over him.

"We left there, legally. Coincidences can happen, yet you read into everything. Other nurses can and do exist."

"I know," I say in a meek, timid voice. "The way she looked at me, though. I felt it. I felt the way that she stares at me. I swear that was her."

"So what if it was? You're free. We're here, not there. This is exactly what I wanted to talk to you about."

"What's that?"

"What you just did." He's pointing in the direction of the nurse. "You've never acknowledged me to other people. You try to make me leave or you'll walk silently by my side."

"She saw me talking! I don't understand it, but all the other times we've been separated were when we talk around other people."

"Ever thought of introducing me?" The truth is that I have, but don't want to. I need him. He allows me to be strong, to look other people in the eye and know that I'm not alone. When I am with him I am above their gaze. They only wish they were with someone like him, someone whose appearance commands respect. That's why they make him leave: jealousy. I won't let them have him, not even hear his voice.

"There will be time," I respond. "Let's just keep walking."

"No, I have something to tell you. You've been getting worse. The last time we were together, it was as if you were looking through me."

"We were in an asylum! I was a patient! God knows why I was there, but that's where it's the worst." I notice another figure walking towards us, her hands held tightly to her side and a gaze fixated outwards into nothing and I continue. "How did you even manage to get in there? And it wasn't a visit, but for days. Did you notice how they took you away as soon as we spoke?"

"Yet you're talking right now." His voice is like venom as the woman walks past.

"She's living in her head. We were fine."

"I've moved on. It's been years. I don't know if you've felt it, but the years have passed. " The venom is spreading slowly from my fingers and up my arms. "I promised you that I'd get you out of that ward. Now I truly can move on with a clean conscience and you can move on and start living."

"I just started living and it's already ending." My tears are flowing, following contours, leaving trails. "You don't know what it's like waiting for someone in there. They judged and ripped me to pieces with their eyes. I never talked to anyone. I sat alone with my books. I waited with my chair facing outwards toward the window every day, for who knows how long. I will never know now. They kept me on those pills." The venom slithers up my chest and is traveling through the veins of my neck. The soupy, atmospheric pond returns to a murky brown.

"I never wished this on you. But there's nothing I can do." The woman walks between us again. She looks through me.

"Let's just figure this out, please," I say. The clouds tear apart, every one of them.

Make them stop! No! This is real! The pond's serene shores fold, gather up, and place themselves again upon the walls; I only see my black and brown complexion.

"I'm sorry. I can't love you anymore," he says. Not yet, not yet. I need him. He can't leave me like this. The venom causes my ears to ring, the tiles cold under my feet.

"I know you can. Just say you can." The venom numbs my lips and he fades away, leaving me standing in front of the mirror with foul, brown eyes. The poison fades slowly, yet I pray for it to remain. He's done this before. I can wait.

SOUR LIVER VODKA

MARGARET O'BRIEN

Remember the day you put pierogi in the suitcase
in Poland; you flew
across the continent

Later, together we swam up Market Street drowned St Andrews red
in afternoon
you bought green-skinned leeks, long and thick like children's arms
white-spooned sour cream
butter from the barrel
Żołądkowa from the man just off the square
all sad blue eyes,
Irish, and homesick?

You sizzled them in a borrowed frying pan
we toasted gold wódka and golden dumplings
our smiles filling cold like water into paper cups
stomachs heavy, heavy hooks holding us fast
to that strange Scottish town.

Afterward, walking out to West Sands to see
the gravel-voiced seals, grey as the breakers
and the sheep on the hills so far away, enough to be
just flecks of lint on the rolled over land
the arched backs of tellurian beasts
that still slumber, slumber and sleep?

21 GUN SALUTE

BEN ALFARO

for richard snyder, scott walker, richard scott

draconian—*adj* 1. red, in flurried spray. 2. there is penance in this, a reward equally brawn; a pistol as big as yours. 3. all attica behind your sword, like hammurabi before him; them before you. 4. creaking of my mother's stiff back, slit; still chasing this american dream. 5. brazen commitment to stay daydreamer. easier to herd the sheep.—*noun* 6. a fourth degree burning, charred black; your body an ember, your hands, face, calves, chest: coal. 7. from *draco:* a northern dragon swinging in constellation; the breathing back in flame; it's all red, anyway. 8. union, pedagogue, social servant: bullet. 9. blood. 10. (*used with object*) bloodfight. 11. prisons *are* obsolete. are more valuable than schools. are indicative of values. 12. the man guillotined be the same man who invented it; there is no irony in that. *-verb* 13. to accost your reasoning; to be the same idea you seek to destroy. 14. to sever the state by way of dismissing the people. 15. to bleed, it's all red anyway. 16. to read the news. say some things don't change. 17. must think we crazy, some demon must've caught us dreaming. again. 18. to falsely attribute; pruneface reagan is legend, eyesore, icon—would've probably not been your friend. probably not been red. 19. to wonder which nerd kills school. 20. to chew the idea of rebellion, gather the pitchfork from the barn, solder these beliefs in the alloy. 21. to chance a sleeping wolf's food; run when his bite sounds sharper than his bark. to blood let for blood shed, it's coming.

MY SEMESTER ABROAD

MSU Flash Fiction Contest Winner

BY XIU LI ZHENG

LYNETTE SCORE

During my semester at Michigan State University, I learned about Hell from the preacher at Wells Hall. Every afternoon he would shout at me across the courtyard that I was going to go there and I would almost spill my tea. But I didn't spill my tea—I would force myself to stare at my shoes and ignore him like everybody else: the boy who was going to Hell because he was homosexual, the gray-haired professor who was going to Hell for wearing headphones, the girl who was going to Hell because she had words on the backside of her pink sweatpants.

I didn't know what Hell was. I had only heard the word one time before, in China, in a film that Yao and I had watched for our American Cinema class. I don't remember the name, but there was a character in the film who was a TV news reporter and shouted in the middle of a broadcast, "I'm mad as Hell and I'm not going to take it anymore!" It caused everyone else in America to open their windows in the middle of a storm and shout it as well. I wondered afterward what kind of word "Hell" was, to make people act like that. I asked Yao.

"I don't know," she said. "I know it's from Christian religion."

That was probably all she thought about it, but I had been proud so far to have understood everything about American language and culture. I read books in English and received top marks in all of my American Studies classes. What if Hell was really important?

I went to the government church the next Sunday, but it was very tiresome and nobody said anything about Hell. I didn't go so far as to attend an underground church. One girl I knew had done that for several weeks in a row and then disappeared.

So I had to satisfy my curiosity with what I heard in America from the Wells Hall preacher. I learned something new about Hell from him almost every day. I learned that Hell was a place where people could go after they died—which didn't make very much sense. I also learned that Hell was a very bad place to be and that it had a whole lake made out of fire. You could never, ever get out. I learned that Hell was where the devil lived. I was familiar with the devil, but I had not known that he was real.

After a while, I became very afraid of the things that the Wells Hall preacher was talking about. I really did not want to go to Hell. I found myself thinking about Hell all the time and sometimes I would have nightmares that I was in Hell and that the devil was hurting me. I tried to talk to my roommate about it. She was American, but she just said not to worry about it.

One day, after reminding us all that we were going to go to Hell, the preacher said, "But believe in the Lord Jesus Christ and you will be saved."

I was so relieved. There was something I could do, something I could believe so that I wouldn't have to go to Hell! I dropped my tea on the ground and ran all the way across the courtyard, pushing people out of my way, and when I finally laid my hands on his shoulders it was like turning on a light switch when you are becoming afraid of the dark.

"Please!" I said, "Please tell me, who is Lord Jesus Christ?"

The preacher looked at me like I had hit him in the face with a hammer. Then he lowered his Christian Bible from where he had held it high in the air.

"How to find him?" I asked.

For the first time ever, the preacher had nothing to say. I was so angry. I shook him and began to speak louder and louder. "I do not want to go to Hell! Please, you have to tell me who is Lord Jesus Christ and how can he help me! Do you even know him?"

The preacher shook his head and finally answered me: "No." His voice was very quiet. "I never have."

He left me standing there in the middle of the courtyard with everybody staring at me.

I never saw him again for the rest of my semester in the United States. I still dream about him sometimes, though. He tries to tell me about Lord Jesus Christ, but when he speaks his words come out twisted and I cannot understand what he says.

IN ALL HONESTY

MSU Prose Contest Winner

CORRINE PRATT

I could begin this letter by asking how you are. I could say something like, "Hello," or, "It's been a long time." I won't do those things, though, because I'm sure you know that it's been a long time, and because if I saw you on the street, I wouldn't say "Hello."

I won't ask you how you are, maybe because I don't know what I want the answer to be, or maybe because I don't care. Maybe I don't care how you are now, only how you will be once this letter is finished. Maybe I only care if you'll change.

I could say that I miss you, but I'm not sure if that's true.

So, now that we have eliminated those possibilities, what's left? The letter has been started, and unless I throw it away, even if I never send it, something must be said. So I suppose I will settle for saying that when I told Erika I would be writing to you, she asked if I would be honest. I told her that I would be as honest as I ever am, which is not at all really, and she said that was for the best. She said you would be expecting that. Expecting a string of half-truths. She was always rooting for you, Erika was.

Do you know that I am engaged? I thought maybe that someone had told you. Did you smile when you learned? Did your features tense for a moment against your will? Or did you laugh, disbelieving? What were the words you said upon hearing it? "I'm glad for her," or, "It should have been me," "I hope never to see her again," "I hope she's happy," "I hope she's miserable"?

I think it's safe to say that I've examined every possibility.

There are many things that I could say about my fiancé. I could tell you that his hair is so blonde it's nearly white, that his jaw is wide but his chin sharp. I could say that he owns a store, or that he frowns in his sleep, his eyebrows pulling slightly inward.

I feel, however, as though these details won't interest you, so I will say merely that when I met him, I was attracted to him immediately, if only for the fact that he wasn't you.

Erika and I had lunch today, as we do every week. I found it difficult to enjoy her company when she was constantly reprimanding me, telling me that I should be wearing my engagement ring, or pestering me, asking about this letter.

I am sure you remember how Erika can be.

Erika is going to be my maid-of-honor.

She asked about this letter, as I should have expected her to. She asked why it is that I am writing to you, and, frankly, I am not sure of the reason. Am I trying to make you jealous? Trying to rekindle an old romance? Or merely hoping to reconnect with a lost friend? I'm not sure.

There I go again, being dishonest. There was a lie in that last paragraph, did you catch it?

My fiancé and I met at a "Singles Mixer." A bit sad, isn't it? Erika was surprised I went, and I admit I was ashamed to tell her about it in the first place. What a sad place to meet somebody, what a pathetic story to tell someday, should everything go according to plan. "My husband and I met at a Singles Mixer." When I told her, she asked me, "Do you really want to be someone's girlfriend? Or do you just want to be able to tell people that you have a boyfriend?"

When I told her I was engaged, she asked do I really want to marry him, or do I just want to be married.

Do you have a girlfriend? Is that an appropriate question to ask? You aren't here to say no, so I will ask it anyway. Are you someone's boyfriend? Are you going to be someone's husband?

On second thought, I don't want to know. It's not important.

Please excuse the change in pen. A letter this strange always demands more than one day to write, and this one has demanded several. I will not tell you exactly how long it has taken me, because I am embarrassed at how long it takes me to get this honest. This honest, of course, not being very honest.

This morning, Erika and I went to the dress store. To buy a dress. For my wedding. All these women there, about to get married, all excited, all talking, all crying. When I was in the dressing room, the woman in the stall next to mine asked, "Can't you just see it? Being married?"

I did not immediately think of some domestic scene, of cooking breakfast for my husband, of doing his laundry, of the two of us making love in the bed we share. Instead, I saw myself in some vague location, in a store, at the hairdresser, on the street. I saw myself talking to some shadowy figure, talking about "my husband."

If I am being honest, and I rarely ever am, I was less interested in the idea of having a husband than in the idea of telling people that I had a husband.

At this point, I am wondering if perhaps this letter is surprising you. Perhaps it is not meeting up to your expectations. Did you think I would beg you to come back to me? Or I would wish you to be as happy as I, now engaged, have become?

No, unfortunately, that is not this letter. This letter, as everything else, is just me.

When I told my mom I was engaged, she said, "I never thought this day would come." She told me she thought I would always "ruin everything." Always "sabotage" myself. She said, "Like you did with that last boy. The nice one. What was his name?" That last boy. The nice one. You.

Is that what happened? I sabotaged myself? I "ruined everything?" On second thought, don't tell me. I don't want to know.

Do you remember earlier, when I lied? Have you figured out now where it was? It was when I said I didn't know why I was writing to you. That wasn't true. I know exactly why.

Today I was going for a walk and I passed a little girl with her parents, feeding the ducks by the river. Right at the water's edge, where we used to sit on the grass together. Do you remember how you used to get mad at me for feeding the ducks? Do you remember how you would tell me that it makes the ducks dependent on the people who feed them, so much so that they forget they are ducks?

I think of you when I walk by the river and when I wear my red dress and when I go to sleep at night.

Do you have a girlfriend to feed the ducks with? To buy dresses for? To go to sleep with? Don't tell me. It doesn't matter. I don't want to know.

See what I did there? When I said I didn't want to know? I do that so I can ask you any question I want without seeming too curious. Too nosy. Without seeming like I still care. But it's never true. I always want to know.

I wonder, would you believe me if I told you that this is the most honest letter I have ever written?

I'm having trouble sleeping again. Do you remember, how I used to lie awake? I was doing better, for a while. My doctor thinks it's because I've moved in with my fiancé, and the change in routine is causing me anxiety. Erika thinks that it's because I stay up, waiting for something. "Waiting for what?" I asked her, and she told me that that was for me to find out.

Erika never does make anything easy.

My fiancé bought his tuxedo today. For the wedding. For our wedding. When he told me, I must admit, I wasn't very interested. When I imagine our wedding, I see myself walking down the aisle, but I'm not interested that it's him at the end of it.

As always, I only care about myself.

Don't kid yourself by thinking that I would be more interested in my fiancé, were you my fiancé. Don't think that I would think of you more, that I would love you more.

Did you catch it? The lie in the last paragraph? I may be self-centered, but I'm not heartless. I may be a hopeless narcissist, and I may be a liar, but I always loved you.

My mother asks about you. All the time. Whenever I call her on the phone, she mentions you as soon as she thinks she can, without it seeming like she liked you better than she likes my fiancé. She asks, have I seen you? Have I heard from you? Do I miss you?

If I'm being honest, and this is the most honest I've ever been, I am forced to answer no, no, yes.

Earlier, when I said that when I imagine being married, I imagine telling someone that I have a husband? I wasn't being exactly honest then. I don't imagine telling someone, I imagine telling you. I wonder why it is I want you to know. Is it because I want to make you jealous? I want to make you sad? I want to make you wish you're the one I'm going to marry?

Yes, yes, yes.

Am I writing this letter to make you jealous? To rekindle an old romance? To reconnect with a lost friend?

Yes, yes, yes.

I like to imagine that you are happy as you're reading this, that you're smiling fondly as you remember me, each word reminding you of my quirks, of my charm, of our love. Are you smiling? Or are you sad, or angry, or bored? Have you changed, reading this letter, or were you already too jaded, too wary of me for me to reach you? I think it's safe to say I've examined all of the possibilities.

I am getting married in two months. Maybe. Maybe my wedding is in two months. Or maybe you are smiling as you read this. Maybe you're going to write me a letter back. Maybe you're going to tell me that you'd like to be the one I'm engaged to, the person who will be my husband. Maybe you'll ask if I have to have a husband, wouldn't I like for him, out of everyone, to be you?

I like to think you're going to write me a letter back. I like to think that in two months, when I walk down the aisle, you will be the one at the end of it.

CHARISSA KIM **HUNGER**

PARADOX ALORA WILDE

© Andrea Bartley, "Benjamin"

ANDREA BARTLEY **BENJAMIN**

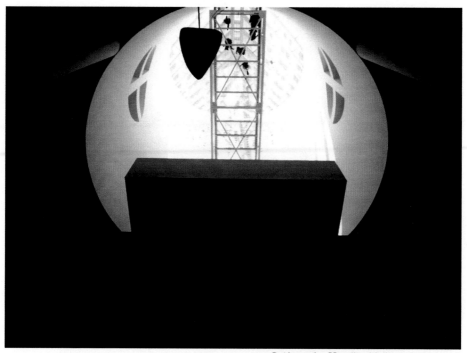

ARCHITEKTON-
ARCHIMAGO

ALEXANDRA HAY

© Chase O'Black, "Strike a Pose"

CHASE O'BLACK

STRIKE A POSE

MSU Visual Art Contest Winner

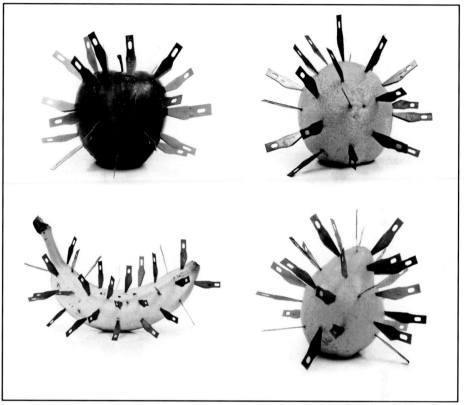

© Andrew Phillips, "Fruit"

FRUIT ANDREW PHILLIPS

MSU Visual Art Contest Winner

PHILLIPS 39

© Shira Golden Kresch, "Mobo"

SHIRA GOLDEN KRESCH **MOBO**

MSU Visual Art Contest Winner

40 GOLDEN KRESCH

LOOKING FOR
ASTRONAUTS

DANA DIEHL

I tear into a can of sardines, and I'm reminded of my husband. It's been three months since Liam was shot into space, and they say that after two hours the fluids in your body shift, swelling up your face, your ears, your hands. The swelling goes down, but then a month goes by and your bones begin to deteriorate.

I sit on the back porch and look across at the shadow of pine trees, pulling the sardines apart with my fingers. Their backbones fall out like butter, cream white and delicate in my palms. Liam always missed the tiny wing bones when he grilled chicken out back, and I expect the vertebrae to feel like that, rough and hard. But no, these are soft. I put the bones on my tongue because I want to know what vertebrae taste like, and because I grew up being told to never waste anything. I chew and I feel them break, dissolve against my gums. Effortless.

I think of Liam and his baby-soft bones, and of the pamphlets sitting on my counter for wives who have been left for space. I think about how astronauts return to land and the pressure of being on earth again breaks them.

It's a strange feeling, knowing your husband is no longer on the planet. They tell us it takes eight minutes for the space shuttle to reach outer space, and I count backwards from the moment the shuttle launches. I count through the stratosphere, the mesosphere, the thermosphere, and suddenly there are no numbers left, and Liam is gone.

I told him last night, killing mosquitoes against our flesh on the hotel balcony, not to leave. Tam and John were bouncing from bed to bed inside the room, beach sand falling from their skin into the sheets like fairy dust. I moved onto Liam's lap, pulling him against me, and his bare scalp felt odd against my cheek. I'd shaved it the night before so that it wouldn't get in his way during his eight months in space, shaved it until it looked as raw and shiny as a peeled onion. Afterward, I ran my hands over it, trying to find something familiar, but it was like when they cleared a patch of the forest to put in phone lines. All the softness was gone. Even now, placing my palm against his crown, there was just a roughness that I didn't recognize.

Please stay with us, I said into his ear. But up into the sky he went.

The launch is so much faster than I expect it to be. It's a flash of orange and a shimmer of exhaust, and then the shuttle is moving upward. The thunder of the engines and the firework-pop of the rockets rolls over our viewing pad twenty seconds late, and even after the shuttle disappears, like a white, burning seagull on the horizon, I can hear it singing in my ears.

Afterward, Tam, John, and I return to our log house in the woods, where it's nothing but indigenous forests and lakes for miles and miles. I take the kids into the forest, where the sky is leafy instead of vast, so we can feel connected to the earth again. Florida was all sand and blue, and I miss the rich colors of upstate New York.

Tam and John find the skeleton almost immediately. It's white and innocent looking, sorrel inching its way around its edges. Tam tells me it's human. She's taking human anatomy this summer, so she should know. She counts the ribs one at a time, numbering them under her breath like they learned during the fetal pig dissection.

"Don't touch," she warns. John tosses the leg bone toward her like a boomerang. It lands in the fern, but she shrieks. She loses count.

The skeleton must have been lying here for months. Or maybe it was only days. The ribs are curved and white, and it's incredible to me how much they resemble the bottom frame of a ship. People could be carried out to sea in those ribs. I wonder what a person's ribcage reveals about them. Running my fingers over my abdomen, I feel for any cracks or growth rings Tam or John might have left behind. Growth that came from me, but also from Liam.

"Not human," John concludes. He holds up a skull, brushing off a skin of wet dirt. It's long and mean-looking with hollow eyes. I imagine sticking my thumb and forefinger into the holes like it's a bowling ball. But no, this is the wrong shape. It would bounce, crack, once it hit the polished lane.

"Ew! You can see scratch marks," says Tam. She takes the skull and cradles it in both hands. I wonder what kind of mother I am for not stopping her. The germs that must be on it. But I see the way she rubs her thumbs over the raised cheek bones like it's a sleeping cat that must be stroked awake, and I can't stop her. I feel weird knowing that part of me is in those fingers.

"It was the crows," says John, "Picking away the flesh with their beaks."

"Don't make me picture it!" Tam sets the skull down in the sorrel. The flowers aren't blooming yet, and it'd be easy to mistake them for clovers. She rests her hands on her knees. "It was a deer, by the size of it. You think?"

"Probably."

John picks through a pile of leg bones, collapsed into a pile in the brush. He holds two long, thin slivers of the tibia crossed between his fingers like chopsticks and mimes eating something long and stringy out of the skull's eye hollows, until Tam knocks them out of his hands. Then he finds the bullet, embedded in the vertebrate pressed between the skeleton and the sorrel leaves.

"Get it out," Tam says.

But his fingers slip, and he has to borrow one of her straight bobby-pins to pry it from the disc of bone. When it's done, he turns to me for the first time. "Look."

My palm opens out of instinct, and he drops the bullet into it. It falls heavy, and I close my fingers. The bullet is smooth and solid and colder than I expected. I'm disappointed. Part of me wanted it to be hot, fiery with the kill, like something alive.

I drop it into my jean shorts pocket, and I feel the downward nudge against my hips. I beckon to Tam and John, and we make our way back to the house.

I remember the moment I decided I never wanted to live alone. I was twelve, and I had learned about asthma in class that day. Hours later, crouched, my back pressed flat against the cold wall in the hallway, I was afraid I had it. I felt the cavities in my lungs, and no matter how many breaths I took, they didn't seem to fill up. My fingers clutched at the carpet coils, and I folded myself into a cricket position, as though it might help me suck the air into my body. It seemed ridiculous, breathing. You inhale, you save yourself. And then two seconds later you have to do it again. It can never stop, and I was afraid it would. I was afraid that I would die here, empty and unseen.

My parents weren't home; they were at a party that made my mom pull a string of pearls out from the bottom of her sock drawer. I tried to imagine calming things. I thought of gray, stone beaches that smelled of cold stone and had no push and pull of water, just a quiet seaside with mute, white birds. I thought of Easter morning and of foil-shelled eggs nestled in plastic straw. I thought of a man, warm-smelling and kind, who would never leave me behind for parties. I could picture his back best in my mind, shoulder blades making dents in his shirt. I loved those shoulder blades. They made me wish that hugs went backwards.

It's been three months since Liam left, and I can't remember what it feels like to be in my body. I am a floating mind. I look in the mirror, and I'm surprised to see my face. But even then, it's just a reflection, a throwback of light particles, nothing I can touch. From day to day, I only see my kids, who are detached from me, who live their separate lives in the same house. Their conversations with me aren't real conversations; they're clipped comments over dinner. I feel like my body disappears.

I find a Polaroid camera with extra film in the closet, wrapped in Liam's folded red sweater. I sit on the floor, back against the bed and aim the camera at my face. I stare into the black lenses and pretend I'm staring into a lover's face. I let my face melt, burning like the feeling you get when you swallow hot chocolate at a cold football game and feel it warming down your throat. I hold onto that feeling and snap. Before the picture forms, I try another face. This time, I'm desperately sad. Snap. I try a third expression, open-mouthed, teeth-bearing laughter.

I place the three Polaroids in a line on the carpet and watch my faces form in the light. This is what people will see when they look at me.

The in-love face dries first. I'm unhappy with the result. I thought I'd been smiling in a quiet, content way, but my lips look thin and stretched. My eyebrows are raised, making me look like someone who might scold you for talking too loudly or for not saying "thank you." Is this what Liam saw that morning when he left me for space?

Before sadness and laughter can form, I scoop the photos into a pile and toss them in the waste basket.

We keep the lights off in the evenings, and I say it's to save electricity and to keep the moths from being drawn to our windows. They always tear their wings against our metal screens. We wander through dark hallways, not really knowing which room we're going to, bumping into each other and asking names into the dark. "Tam?" "No." "John?" John likes the dark. He gets his flashlight and creates cones of light against the wall, experimenting with the different shapes his hand can make and the shadows they cast. Tam plants herself in front of the television, flitting between Discovery and Animal Planet. I sit on the back porch, smelling the forest, tracing the constellations with my eyes, waiting for them to fill the void.

John's been watching alien movies. I don't know where he got them. I hid all the space movies once we knew Liam was going into orbit. Things never work out for astronauts in films—think Apollo 13 or Tim Robbins in Mission to Mars—and I didn't want the kids seeing that. But somehow John gets a hold of Independence Day and gets it into his head that we need to learn to live off the land in case of an out-of-this-world invasion. Hunting and skinning rabbits in our backyard. Scavenging for wild raspberries. Learning to extract water from tree limbs if the well is contaminated.

He says fried frog legs are a traditional meal in rural Pennsylvania. A friend told him they're crunchy, like deep-fried peas, and salty like chicken. I tell him that's gruesome, but he goes off into the woods toward lake. He has the pointed stick we use to roast marshmallows rested over his left shoulder. I think about stopping him, but the John walking away from me looks so much like Liam, it stops me in my tracks.

He comes back later with no frogs, but hands full of water and tadpoles. I run outside with an empty peanut butter jar, licked clean by the dog.

"There weren't any frogs," he tells me, tipping the squirming black puddle into the jar.

There's barely any creek water left in his hands, and the tadpoles slip and struggle against each other. I fill it up the rest of the way using the hose.

"Maybe we should stick with living off of plants," I say.

I pull out a book on wild plants in Northern Appalachia to learn which are safe to eat, but I get lost in the names of mushrooms. They are all called things like Devil's Urn, Old Man of the Wood, Scaly Tooth, and Beefsteak Polypore. I walk into the forest alone, holding the book in front of me like a map. I read that mushrooms like cool, dark places, so I head for the lake, stomping through fern forests and rotten logs and brambles that stick to the high, gray socks I pull over my ankles.

The lake is gray and still under a close, overcast sky when I reach it. I find a circle of small, orange mushrooms growing from a bed of pine needles, and I leaf through the book, trying to identify them. But they aren't there. Or, I'm not looking in the right places.

I think about how when I was little, my mom told me that a circle of mushrooms was called a fairy ring, and that you should never step inside that circle or the fairies would steal you away into their underground kingdom. I believed her. I never stepped inside. But as I stand alone in the forest now, drops of hard rain disrupting the lake and leaving dark spots on my shoulders, part of me wants to be taken away. I step into the circle and sit cross-legged in the dirt, like I haven't sat in so many years. I stare out at the lake, waves of warm rain-air pulling up goose bumps on my arms, and I wait.

You would think that the greatest danger in space is the radiation or cold. But it's actually the nothingness that kills you. The vacuum. Exposed to space without protection, you lose consciousness in nine seconds. In two minutes, your blood boils and you die.

I wonder what those nine seconds are like before the deoxygenated blood reaches your brain. For nine seconds it would only be you floating in space, stars tangling in your hair and catching in the corners of your eyes like gnats. I imagine it would be exhilarating. I imagine it would be lonely.

For a few weeks after the launch, everyone visits me. Everyone is full of questions about if I'm sad, if I'm scared. They all think I'm brave, living my life as my husband orbits overhead. They talk about how courageous he is, leaving behind a family, an entire planet. As though it's a difficult thing to do.

At night here, there's nothing to fade out the stars. When Liam's family or old college friends make the drive up to visit me, I like to point at satellites moving across the sky and say, "That's my husband. I see him every day, up there in the sky." I say it while holding a plate of corn on the cob or kielbasa, leaning against the back patio.

I never know if I'm right. I could be pointing at anything. Liam explained to me before he left that the space station travels at 17,227 miles per hour and completes 15.7 orbits around the earth every day, doing experiments in anti-gravity and exercising and plotting the stars. I try to work out which country he would be over at different points in the day. It makes Liam feel more real if I can say, "He's in the Czech Republic until two" or, "Oh, he's sucking freeze-dried soup out of a pouch over Singapore today." But he moves so fast, and I've never been any good at math.

I realize I'm waiting. Waiting for Liam to send word to me or to offer me a way to follow him like he always did. As the weeks pass, I try to calculate other, simpler things on the corner of the morning newspaper above the Sudoku squares. Like how many sunrises and sunsets he's seen. In three months, I've seen one hundred and fifty-two. Liam has seen exactly twelve hundred.

Leaning against the back of my kitchen chair, John asks me if we can mail him the bullet we found in the woods. He figures we can send it up in a smaller rocket ship, it will get to Liam in three days. Three days. That's forty-eight sunrises and sets.

What can I be to Liam when I am a single sunrise and sunset in a day? What am I when the earth is something he can hold in the palm of his hand?

John never takes his tadpoles back to the lake, and I don't press him to. I move their jar to the back step and watch as little nubs of legs sprout from their bellies, elbows first. I never noticed how tadpoles move together, like schools of fish. I wish

I could stunt their growth in this in-between stage. I wonder if they know that one day they'll grow up and leave one another.

This is the relationship of a girl and an astronaut:

We met on a jet plane flying over the Atlantic. I was twenty-two, just out of school with a B.A. in public finance, heartbroken and looking to forget in European cathedrals and canals. I wanted badly to lose my memory to languages that had no meaning to me. I had poured my bank account into the plane ticket. I didn't know where I was sleeping that night.

Liam, in a hoodie with boyish legs and high, white socks, was visiting friends in France. He told me that he would take care of me, that I could stay at his hostel that night. I melted. I swore I would never leave him.

For the next two weeks, we traveled together. He moved, and I followed. We shared jars of peanut butter for dinner because it was all we could afford and it was the only thing he could pronounce in French. We snuck into fancy restaurants just to pee in free toilets. We saw every church in every city, because it was a place to go when it rained, and took pictures with disposable cameras of funny-looking ladies on the street who dressed their dogs in scarves and vests.

Then he returned to America, and I followed. For two years we called and lettered. Then we moved into an apartment in Boston together. He was studying astronomy, and I could fall asleep at night to talk of supernovas and the expanding universe. I dreamed of us floating through the meteor belt together. Then he proposed. Then we got married. So it goes.

The space shuttle gets the web cams working, and soon we're able to talk with Liam for an hour one evening in August. I turn on the webcam fifteen minutes before I know he'll be there, playing with the lights, the camera angle. I realize my best angle is from slightly above, emphasizing my long face, my eyes.

"Hello, earthlings," he greets us. Suddenly Liam is there, a five by five box of monochrome pixels on the computer screen. He speaks in an E.T. voice, holding up the Spock fingers.

"How are my kiddos?" He grins, bobbing up and down. The movement unnerves me.

"Rich Stanzione got caught cheating off of me on the Anatomy final," Tam tells him.

"I fed a firefly to a toad," says John.

I study him as he talks to our children. I notice his white astronaut suit, soft-looking like a pair of pajamas. I notice the top of his head, shaped like the bottom of an eggplant, covered in new blonde fuzz. I think of the night I shaved it for him, how his yellow locks fell on my toes and how I kept finding them on clothing or in the carpet for weeks.

"And how are you, babe?"

Liam's eyes shift so he's looking me in the eyes, and I feel a rush of warmth. I smile, and his expression doesn't change as he stares back at me. I realize it's not my eyes he's staring into, but the black, shiny lenses of the camera.

"I'm fine."

I watch his face move on the screen and try to remember what it felt like to touch him. It's amazing how quickly you forget things like that.

Later, when the kids leave—John getting ready for bed and Tam studying for a test in the morning—Liam leans closer to the camera.

"How are you really?"

"I'm hanging in there."

"You know, I wish you were here." It's a mess of control panels behind him, all very white and sterile. I search the background for signs of familiarity, for a little bit of me. Liam is all over this house: photographs, dirty handprints on door frames. In space but still grounded. I wonder if part of me is in the spaceship with him, but it all looks so foreign. No photos, no handkerchiefs soaked in my perfume.

"Me too," I say.

"I miss you at night."

I nod. He feels so far away right now. I look at his jawbone, the space where his eyebrows almost connect, his ear lobe. I try to recognize something in his face that I could touch once. But the harder I look, the more his face dissolves into pixels of colored light.

Tam tells me they watched a birth in human anatomy today. It was on an old VHS tape, but still you could see everything. The mother gave birth in a kiddy pool in the center of her living room. Tam says she never wants to be a mother.

I loved being pregnant. I talk to other mothers, and they say I'm crazy. They complain about stretch marks, about their changed center of gravity, about not feeling sexy anymore. But those things don't mean anything, really. I loved looking at diagrams of the pregnant body, the way that the fetus looks like a curling green leaf inside an acorn. Thinking about it that way made me feel warm, like I was part of the earth. I even loved the implications of the word pregnant. In the red-bound dictionary, it's defined as rich in significance or implication. Having possibilities of development or consequence.

I wish Tam had never seen the VHS. Birth is pain and things breaking and a separation. We shouldn't know what we came from, not that early.

There's a thunderstorm over the woods that night, and I wake up tangled in sheets on Liam's side of the bed. It's the first time I've done this, let my unconscious body cross that invisible line. I'm angry at my body. It's getting used to Liam's absence. It's accepting that he's left. It feels that empty space, and instead of curling into itself, becoming denser, it's using this space to spread.

I groan. I flip myself roughly onto my stomach, burying my face into Liam's pillow. I gulp at the air, like I've seen goldfish do, and try to find Liam's scent somewhere in the pillowcase. It smells of fabric and eucalyptus.

Thunder rumbles. I can hear the storm moving the entire forest. I un-stick myself from the mattress and move to the window, pulling aside the curtains. Rain beats against the metal screen. Lightning turns the high, dark tips of the pine trees into a moving silhouette.

I'm alone in my little bubble, in my room that still has that stuffy smell of warm sleep. No one can hear me or see me, and it makes me feel invincible. I want to pick up the phone and dial the numbers of old boyfriends, talk to them until I'm sure my voice still works. I want to slide open my window, climb down the roaring drain pipe, and walk barefoot across the puddling backyard and into the woods. And then what? I don't know, but I realize I can do these things, and this realization gives me a thrill. When I don't do these things, I feel disappointed in myself. The disappointment makes the moment pass.

I crawl back into bed and arrange the blankets around my neck and have unsettling dreams about being a child again, looking for life in shells I find washed up on the beach. I kick and kick at the bed sheets, at the sand, wanting to upturn mollusks and cuttlefish and nautilus. But my toes never come in contact with those hard, rounded surfaces. I find only sand.

Tam and John are out back looking for astronauts. The space station is scheduled to orbit over our part of the sky at 11:17 PM. By ten, they're lying on their backs in the grass, binoculars aimed skyward. I watch them out the window over the kitchen sink, the dark blurring the binoculars and their faces into one. These are my children: long, bug-eyed creatures.

I join them an hour later, carrying my good camera out on a tripod. I want to capture the moment the satellite streaks across the sky. The night is perfect. Cool and clear, the stars so bright and close I feel like I could scoop them, pebble-like, into my palm.

The station is said to take twenty-five seconds rise and fall against the horizon. I set the camera shutter to stay open for thirty, watch the second hand on my watch, and click when Tam shouts that she sees something to the west. We look to the sky.

It looks much like a satellite, but brighter, more lights. It moves with purpose.

"That's it, right?" John asks. I nod in the dark.

"Wave hi to your dad," I murmur.

And we do wave. Three lonely bodies, upturned faces white like snowdrops, invisible on the dark part of the earth.

You never see the moment the tadpoles change from tadpoles into frogs. One day they're black drops in a jar of water, tails sucking back into their spines, then their nubby legs burst from their rubbery flesh. And then the jar is empty. Two weeks later, you'll see something gray hopping across the black pavement of the driveway. You think it's a cricket at first, but something about the unsteady, lost way it moves will make you crouch on your knees, face close to the ground. You catch the miniature frog, only the size of your pinky nail, mid-hop. As it noses and flaps against your cupped fingers, you'll wonder if it's one of your tadpoles. Without its brothers, you can't recognize it.

I read an article the night after Liam orbited over our sky, curled in a towel in the center of my bed, showered hair dripping little, broken stars on the laptop. It says the moon is leaving the earth. Every year, the moon moves 3.8 centimeters farther away from the planet. Tidal bulges in our oceans are slowing it down, giving it a larger orbit. My grandchildren's grandchildren's grandchildren will never see a total eclipse. Their moon will be too far away.

I feel like I should be more surprised, more dismayed than I am. But this is just the way of the universe. Spinning and pulling and spreading things apart.

When I get my film developed later, I flip through photos of Tam and John swimming in the lake, of cardinals in the birdfeeder out the window, of a fern patch after a rainstorm. I stop on the photo I took that night Liam flew overhead. I want to be able to point to the cluster of lights in the sky and have him pinpointed for once. But when I hold the photo up to the light, the station is only a white beam across the photograph. Everything is in streaks. The stars. A satellite. All stuck in a state of moving.

When Liam comes home months later, after ten in space, he won't be able to walk. His legs will be all wobbles and he'll lean on me and I won't recognize the thin, pale face close to mine. I won't recognize the smell on the back of his neck that reminds me of a clean lab table.

During the car ride home, we will be all questions. We'll all want to know what it was like to be in space.

"It's just unbelievable up here," he'll say. "Amazing."

Those are the only words he can ever find. Amazing. Incredible. Breathtaking.

But I can't imagine an adjective. I will ask him more questions.

"What does the sunrise look like from outer space?"

"Could you see the aurora borealis?"

The kids will help.

John: "How do you pee when there's no gravity?"

Tam: "How long will it take you to regain your bone mass?"

But even as he describes the spreading tangerine stain of the sunrise across the planet or the feeling of waking up in the air, I won't be able to put pictures to the words. I won't know how to explain to him that even now, space isn't real to me. It's the kids, eight years younger, playing in the refrigerator box in the backyard, Sharpie-ing in buttons and levers and gauges until it is a spaceship. They have me cut a rectangle out of the front for window, but then make me duct tape it back on when they realize there are just trees and flowers and blue sky outside. They are seven and three. My belly and chest still sag with proof of growing a child. Liam is tan and tight like a rubber band about to snap. When he has us test his eye sight using words Tam scribbles on graph paper or his sense of balance by spinning him on the swings, I still tell made-up stories about the day we'll all go into space and explore the solar system together. Tam dreams of the spaceship flying. She goes out on windy days, seven years old and sturdy enough to steer, hoping a gust of forest air will sweep the ship up. Just a second of flight, that's all she wants. One day, when she's inside, John sneaks alongside the box and pushes it down the hill. Tam is infuriated when she realizes it was him—not because she was bruised and tumbled. But because the spaceship moved, and now she knows it's all pretend.

QUIET
PEOPLE

CARRIE WALKER

The archive center is the color of a manila envelope, has no windows, and smells like dust with only a hint of lemon Pledge cleaner. There are four hundred and fifteen rows of shelves that stretch ten feet into the air like the columns of an ancient structure, each shelf completely full with neatly labeled boxes in chronological and alphabetical order.

Margaret arrives every morning at six am with a thermos of decaf coffee creamed to the light brown color of an old newspaper. She wears her hair in a loose bun, bangs neatly combed in a straight line parallel with her eyebrows. Her clothes add twenty years to her appearance with her muted blouses and charcoal gray skirts and high stockings. Nobody coming into the archive center would guess she's under forty five, though she graduated with her master's degree in historical preservation only two years ago at twenty four. Margaret looks at people's hands when she talks and barely speaks above a whisper.

Around nine, a man enters the building while Margaret is logging a set of police reports from last month. She stands and greets him softly, but he pushes right past her desk and heads for the large room with the shelves, gruffly grumbling, "Maps," and ignoring her offer to show him around. He has hands like baseball gloves, fingers blackened with some sort of oil or dirt and Margaret's brow wrinkles, worrying about smudges and fingerprints. She fumbles with the hem of her sweater and chews her lip, peeking into the room to make sure he at least heads in the right direction.

While Margaret can no longer see the man, she can hear him coughing and snorting and oh, dear lord . . . spitting. She grabs for the Purell pump on her desk and coats her hands in the sanitizer, breathing in the wonderful sharp smell to calm her down. About fifteen minutes pass and she quietly walks into the archive room to ask the man if he's finding everything all right, hands clasped lightly in front of her waist.

"Do you need assistance with anything, sir?" she asks, keeping her distance since he's still hacking like a coal miner. She notices that he's pulled dozens of large maps of the county out onto the viewing table. She sees a large black smudge marring the immaculate ivory of one map and her heart sinks. They're all completely out of order and he's folded several of them and the corners are getting dog eared and God in Heaven is that a soda he has leaving a ring on Main Street?

Not bothering to look up, the man grunts, "No, now leave me alone, lady."

Margaret nods and whispers an apology before turning on her heels and scurrying back to her desk. She takes a few deep breaths, feeling her head spinning. It would take hours to reorganize those maps and even longer to get replacements for the ones he'd ruined. Sitting back down, Margaret takes a mint from the jar next to her Post-It notes and bites it in half.

A loud, "Well, shit!" comes from the archive room and Margaret's stomach twists like a pretzel. She hides behind the shelf with the yearbooks dating back to 1902 and peeks around to see that the man has spilled his Big Gulp soda all over the table . . . all over the maps. Her jaw tightens and she once again retreats back to her desk, but this time she pulls open a drawer and takes out a heavy box filled with tools for maintenance.

She wraps her dainty fingers around the red handle of a wrench and walks quiet as can be back into the room, sneaking up behind the idiot who has desecrated her work. He is bent over, occupied with trying to mop up some of the sticky mess. With one quick swing Margaret knocks him in the side of the head with the wrench and he falls forward onto the table with a smack. Margaret pushes up her sleeves and drags the man's sweaty body across the floor to the storage closet, tugging him by the wrists so she doesn't have to touch his disgusting, germ-infested hands. She covers him with a few trash bags, mapping out in her mind where she would take the body later. The old quarry would probably be best. With the closet door locked, she takes the wrench and climbs a ladder up to the second highest shelf in row 27, stashing it in the box of marriage licenses from November 1938. She efficiently cleans up the mess of soda and maps and returns to logging the police reports.

MY FATHER'S HANDS

ERIK JAMES WILBUR

My father's hands have been calloused hands
since before the stucco won the sunlight war.

He once walked with twelve-gauge and muddy Labrador
where I now park my car.

& at twilight,
the untamed delta breeze still sings their song
though brustling bulrush
like taut horse hair drawn over nickel,
a tune of a distant fiddle,
close enough to hear but not feel.
My father hums the parts he can remember.

And while he scrapes flakes of grease out from underneath his fingernails with a straightened
paperclip he found in the junk drawer in the kitchen,
he surveys his calloused hands,
made to feel the oily wet snap of a mallard's neck,
made for pushing up barbed wire to clear space to step through fences.

He once told me, "pavement's man's best fence,
it's the one that can't be lifted."

And I saw his eyes well up like moonshine—not like the moon shines—
but like a mason jar filled to the brim.

WAITING FOR THE 6: CYPRESS AVENUE, 1982

BEN ALFARO

we've been visitors before.

we've seen the bronx in blazing ruin;
spades expelling gringos to the edge
city and sub-urban, but really never far
from the top.

we take trains underground—cold rail
through beast from beneath it.
my son slung to hip, drenched
in day heat, manhattan
postcard panorama
desiccated and demanding.
all this waiting—watching.

it arrives like a trumpet,
steam escapes from fissures
in the metalwork, scattering.

I pace, we wait to board,
boy asks of the skyline.
how the tide shores
the cityscape into an apex pair:
two steel towers in the air,
squared, stronger than the rest.

(before they hit the floor)

how they derided, looked down
as our ground grew a thick film
of permafrost each year, on nights
we never knew which bellies
could churn themselves full.

lifetimes we spend, becoming accustomed
to just visiting; perpetual transit.

left with ourselves and this distance.
visiting the idea of homeward bound
like two lone kings in a late autumn cage.

SHARK

JULIA HOWLAND-MYERS

We get off the highway east of downtown and pull into a neighborhood behind an abandoned dance club. A wooden fence divides the browning yards from the old club's patio. The spike-shaped tops of some of the fence posts have been broken off and the white paint is chipped. We park on the street at a dead end and get out of the car.

"Ready, Rachel?" I hear the dogs barking. Danny kisses me before I can respond, like he knows what I'm going to say.

"Not necessarily," I say—and I mean it. I had tried to convince Danny to get a rescue, but the guy with the dogs was a friend of a friend. Danny just said, *any dog that gets to become my dog has been rescued.*

Danny had been that kid in the neighborhood who would pretend to run away every other weekend; he'd pack a bag, get as far as the gas station at the highway onramp down the road, and get turned back by the homeless guy who hung out on the curb. When he was thirteen he tried to bring the man home for dinner five Friday nights in a row until his mom called the cops and told them to take *Danny*—no, not the guy in the dirty pajamas with the duffel bag and the cardboard sign. He still liked to make friends in low places. When Danny came back for grad school, he hadn't changed. I hadn't seen him, had barely spoken to him, for eight years.

A man in an oversized basketball jersey comes to the door "Glad you're here. Need to get these dogs off my hands." He motions for us to come inside. We walk past a sofa bed unfolded with tan sheets in a pile and a stack of Playboys on the floor. The place looks like it hasn't been cleaned in months.

There's a whole pack of dogs in the backyard—mutts. One puppy, somewhere around six months old, chews on an old tennis ball. The corner of his floppy left ear is missing.

"Hey big guy." Danny approaches the dog with the ragged ear and scratches its head. It squeaks and rolls over, exposing its spotted stomach.

"Is that him?" I ask Danny.

"Yep. This is Shark. I picked him because of his ear." Shark is all black except when he shows you the spots on his belly.

I nod, and kneel on the yellow grass to rub Shark's stomach. He's panting; he looks like he's smiling. "And the name?"

"That's because of his ear too. Looks like something took a bite out of him. You're a feisty little guy, aren't you Shark?" Danny picks Shark up under his front legs and holds him at eye level. "Alexandra is gonna love him."

Shark sits on my lap on the way back to Danny's place. I'm happy to be taking him away from the dirty house, and I think he's happy to be leaving. He scratches his nails on my corduroy pants, and after he's done that for a few minutes, he licks the spot where he'd been scratching. He does that—he scratches and licks, scratches and licks—all the way home.

❧

Danny's girlfriend Alexandra has curves like a 1950's pinup. I know this because he showed me a picture of her the first time I came over. She's in front of the grey ocean at low tide in a yellow one-piece bathing suit. It's not a prudish one-piece, it's very appealing. Alex's lips are smooth and pushed-out like two skipping stones placed one on top of the other. She blows a kiss at the camera. She is at least 5'7.

"We spent every minute together last summer. Now she's off running around with her pothead cousins in Portland."

When I sat on his bed and he told me about her, and he looked like he missed her, I tried to pretend we were in his backyard, as kids, camped out in the tent. He used to tell me stories about his friends and what happened at school that day. He was two grades ahead of me, so his stories were always fascinating. Sometimes he ended them with "I wish you'd been there." Danny felt like an older brother sometimes, but most of the time when we were together, even as a little kid, I just wished he would hold my hand and never get called into his house for dinner.

"Literally every minute? Together? Wow. That's a lot."

"Don't be that way."

Sometimes when I look at Alex's picture tacked on the wall above Danny's bed

I imagine a giant crab coming out of the ocean behind her and latching its self on to her ankle. She bleeds profusely and she's no longer so smug in her curve hugging one-piece. Sometimes the picture is what I think about before I go to sleep, and I see it on the back of my eyelids, and then it melts. In the morning I wake up and think about how long I should wait to call Danny.

❦

Danny, Shark, and I go to the park down the street from his house. It's morning, and it's June. We drink coffee in mugs we brought from the kitchen and sit on the swings while Shark rolls in the sand. I put out a water bowl for him. I kick off my sandals and gather little rocks into piles with my toes. "Hey Danny?"

"What's up kid?" He turns towards me with that grin that seems to spread through his whole body.

"Can we talk about Alex?"

The grin disappears. "What about her?"

"I mean...why don't you break up with her?"

He kicks the sand with his foot and a little cloud rises into the air. "Would you like it if someone broke up with you while you were across the country for the summer?"

"No, but isn't it better than waiting? I mean, dragging things out? She'll feel like you lied to her." Danny stares at me. His blue eyes look grey when he's angry, at least to me. I see a lot of grey-eyed Danny these days.

"I'm not a liar, Rachel. I'll take care of it. I wish you would just trust me."

Danny turns away from me and leads Shark away from the swings and into the big field to play with the old orange Frisbee.

"I didn't call you a liar," I say, even though I know he can't hear me. I twist around and around in my swing, locking the chains together. I look up, and the trees and the sky blur together like milk swirled in coffee.

I untwist myself and start to swing. I walk my feet along the wet dug out sand until they can't reach any farther. Forward, I point my feet at the trees and pretend I'm going to land in them. Backwards, I look at the trench I've made in the sand and wonder how much it would hurt to fall from the highest point of the swing's curve. On the swing set in my backyard when we were kids, Danny would jump when the swing was almost parallel to the ground, and sail through the air like some kind of super hero. He'd land on his feet every time, bend his knees to absorb the shock of the jump, and pop right back up as if he'd never left solid ground. Then he'd turn around and face me. I was always still on my swing, trying to drag my legs through the air to slow myself down, calculating in my head when it would be safe to leap off.

Once I am low to the ground again I jump. Shark runs to me from the field. I put his leash on. "Let's go. It's too hot out for him."

"Okay. Sorry I lost my temper a little there, Rach." He leans down and kisses me, and pulls me close to him with his hands on my waist. I want to tell him I didn't do anything wrong, but I stay quiet and concentrate on his lips and the ridges of his neck muscles under my hand. Danny is the best kisser. He smells like cigarettes and laundry and I breathe him in. Shark's tail thwaps against my calf.

—❧—

I play with Shark every morning. Danny is taking one class this summer, and most of the time he's still on campus when I get to his house. I let myself in through the screen porch—there is a key under the mat—and refill Shark's water, and give him breakfast. Then we take a walk, and afterwards I get out a tennis ball.

"Go get it, buddy." I throw the ball in a high parabola for Shark. He likes to jump. He can play fetch for ages. I keep a washcloth to grab the balls out of his mouth when we play fetch—they're so slimy, even after the first throw. Shark brings the ball back to me and I throw it again.

Being in Danny's tiny fenced in yard reminds me of when we were kids growing up next door to each other. We both had little yards, but they were twice the size of this one. When I was seven and Danny was ten, Danny's dad wouldn't let him build a tree house on his own—and he refused to do it with any help—so he set up the camping tent in the back yard. He dragged half the stuff from his room out there and called it a fort. I was the only girl he let in. We used to hide there when it rained and pretend we'd be there forever, living off the land.

Shark brings the ball back to me. He smiles and pants, and I rub the edge of that ear. It was healed from the day we got him, but from some reason Shark likes mangled-ear rubs better than anything.

—❧—

In July I sleep at Danny's almost every night. It's too hot to muster the energy to go home. Sometimes we fall asleep on the floor watching movies with the ceiling fan on high, or outside on a blanket drinking beer. Shark wakes me up by licking my face at 5:00 am and I give him a little food so he won't wake Danny up. Sometimes Shark still pees in the house when he gets scared. House training him is slow, because he did whatever he wanted when he lived with the dog man. Those dogs lived like a pack of wolves. If it rains and there's thunder, or if we sleep outside and Shark gets left inside, I have a puddle to clean up in the morning before Danny sees. It's a good thing the floors are wooden.

Tonight we manage to make it to the actual bed to sleep. I lay on my side with my elbow on the pillow and my hand under my ear. Danny runs his finger over my ribcage, down the bend of my waist and over the freckles on my hip. **"Hey Joe"** plays out of his laptop, and he drums his fingers on my thigh, slow and lilting with the beat of the song.

"You are so beautiful."

I laugh.

"No I mean it. You are. I always thought so, even when we were kids. Even when your dad gave you that awful haircut."

I laugh and look away. "What about Alex? She has that whole brown hair and blue eyes thing going on. I love that."

He buries his face in my neck. "You can both be beautiful. But for the record, you are more beautiful."

"Ah, the joys of physical attractiveness. I still wish I had those blue eyes. Or green. Green would work."

Danny sighs and rolls his eyes.

I look at the ceiling. There's a crack in it, and a cobweb where it meets the wall. "Why are you still with her?"

"I thought we finished this conversation the last time we had it."

"You said you would take care of it—"

"Listen. She doesn't come home from Oregon for another month. Relax. You're too uptight." He kisses my forehead. I don't know what to say, so I close my eyes, and burrow into the covers like Shark in his dog bed piled with blankets. I listen to Shark's sleeping breaths.

⌖

Alexandra comes back in August. She has her own apartment, so when Danny gets back from campus early enough we can still have lunch together.

I go to the grocery store and buy bread, cheese, and fruit to bring to Danny's house. I never really learned to cook, but sometimes when Danny's busy he forgets to eat, so I try to bring something over for us to have together on the screen porch. The fan out there makes it almost cool enough.

When I get back to the house from the grocery store, Danny's car is in the driveway. I go in the front door since he's there. "Danny, I brought lunch." I whistle for Shark. "Shark! Food!" I fill Shark's bowl. Then I notice a puddle on the floor. I wonder what would have scared Shark at this time of day. I quickly clean it up and then go into Danny's room. He's on his bed with a textbook open in front of him. "Hey you. I brought food. How was class?" I sit on the edge of the bed. On the wall, Alex smirks in her bathing suit.

"It was alright. I have an exam coming up. Thanks for bringing food."

"I'll get it ready." I walk back into the kitchen. Shark hasn't gotten to his bowl yet. I look outside. The yard is empty except for tennis balls. "Danny, where's Shark?"

"What?"

"Where's the dog, Danny?"

He comes out of the bedroom rubbing his hair back and forth on his head, and stops far away in the middle of the kitchen. "I gave Shark to Alex. Remember that was the plan? When she got home?"

I stare at Danny for a minute, waiting for him to finish the joke. His face is blank. I turn from Danny and walk out to the yard. I lie down in the grass with Shark's tennis balls. I pick one up and throw it in the air. It makes a *thwap* noise when it lands next to my head.

Danny comes outside. He stretches out next to me, takes my hand and holds it, laces our fingers together and rubs his thumb along the outside of my thumb.

I sit up and look into his blue eyes, not seeing him but the lines and spots in the iris, the white space, the black pupil, the molecules. He starts to let go of my hand but I squeeze. I want to ask him if he remembers our fort—how I was the only girl he let in, how we would spend afternoons in there until one day it was gone and we found out his mom had given the tent to Goodwill, no explanation. I want to ask him if he loves me back. I squeeze his hand tighter.

"I have to go, Danny. I'll call you later." I stand up and brush the dirt off my jeans.

"Hey, kid. I'm really sorry about the dog. I thought you understood." Danny reaches out and brushes a strand of hair away from my face.

"Yeah, I'm sorry too." I back away from Danny's hand, turn around, and walk to the driveway through the maze of Shark's tennis balls.

KHOLODNAYA VOYNA

MARIANNE CHAN

You must admit that you have put me in a terrible
Position—I am in love with you and will
Love you until the world becomes cold
In fear of my love; I am only twenty-two, young,
I know that soon you will be old and toothless,
But nonetheless, my love will continue, stubbornly, simply—

For I met you, simply—
In a classroom (I am sure I looked terrible)
Speaking Russian like a baby, my words, dripping, toothless—
But of course I had the will to learn, and I have the will
To love—despite the fact that I am young
And you are (like Moscow in the winter) hopelessly cold

Yet what must one do to combat the cold?
Stay inside, wear layers, clench bodies—contain it, simply.
And I believe the winter of our love is quite young
Flurries falling like baby teeth from the sky, not terrible—
But it is you, the Slavic God of Winter, whose obstinacy will
Stop let the sky's smile become gummy and toothless.

I understand that this poem to you is ineffectual, toothless,
As you are attached and married to that cold
"Beautiful" weasel of a woman (who speaks broken English) and will
Birth two half-weasel half-lovely children, (who will simply
Grow up to be absolutely terrible)—
Wouldn't you want more for your young?

And me? I am still quite young,
American, fertile, vulnerable, though my words are toothless—
I am not yet disenchanted by my world I am not yet terrible,
I have not let the sun dry my brain, nor have I allowed the cold
To smother my choices, to ruin my day, simply:
I have freedoms I have desires that I will

Pursue at will—
The country of my love is still fresh and young
Don't you see? Unlike Russia, who continues to simply
Trudge along, still beautiful, but bruised, tired, nearly toothless
I know that you are centuries older than me, but you are not cold
To the youth, to the freedom of my love! Am I so terrible

(So terrible) that you cannot love me at will?
During the Cold War, I was but a child, still young
Toothless, rebellious, but I am warmer now, and will continue on, simply.

RECIPE FOR CREPES

ANNA WILDFONG

"Elegant, but not extravagant, these thin pancakes are at the same time sturdy and delicate. You can make them just to have around. Keep them stacked on a plate, tightly covered and refrigerated. They will last at least a week—just fill and heat as desired. Wrap crepes around many varieties of foods (a great way to store leftovers!) for different occasions, different times of day. They can quickly transform otherwise ordinary food into something special."—Mollie Katzen

To Prepare Batter:

Crack the eggs and notice how
much more you think about
babies as you get older

You most likely will forget to use
the nonstick pan the first
time you watch your thin spill
of batter turn to a solid sheet
like skin and when you try to lift it
you find it is grafting to the metal
aging into a wrinkled cheek as
you prod it with a wooden spatula

Get out the nonstick you avoid using
because you don't know if it's true
that Teflon gives you cancer
and between flips
think about whether you
are doing the best you can
Note: avoid getting overwhelmed that you
haven't been keeping up with
the New Yorker
or else the kitchen will fill with smoke

Suggested Fillings:

use whatever vegetables you have
and when you cut up tomatoes
wonder if enjoying the way the knife breaks through
and slides into seeds and tomato meat
comes from the reptilian part of the brain
if this sensory pleasure is
like a vestigial organ

In a separate room
keep your books on a shelf (see purées section)
and your records in crates
by the turn table (see breads and other baked goods section)
be very cautious of historical novels
avoid the world music category

pick the diced pieces up with your hand
and recognize they feel something
like the few tongues you
have known well

To Serve:

Take time to stand on a chair and reach
for the Fiestaware plate
pour a glass of water whether
you will drink it or not
set a fork and knife down on a napkin
never pray but sit and eat
as if someone is watching

CONTRIBUTORS

Ben Alfaro is a teaching artist and organizer. He performs with the collegiate poetry troupe *Wordworks* and co-founded *WayneSLAM* on the campus of Wayne State University. He works for InsideOut, Detroit's Citywide Poets program facilitating writing workshops for high school students.

Andrea Bartley is a 2012 BFA candidate for the Milwaukee Institute of Art and Design. She is from Zionsville, IN and moved to Milwaukee, WI to pursue a degree in photography. While in school, she interned for Milwaukee Magazine and her work has been featured in local galleries.

Marianne Chan was born on a crab apple tree in the rural depths of Indianapolis, Indiana. She spent half of her life on three military bases in Germany, and the other half studying Theatre and English in DeWitt, Lansing and East Lansing, Michigan. Her hobbies include jogging, eating raw fish, talking frantically and counting her breaths as the church bells ring. She would like to thank Jack, Patricia, and Rammel Chan, Greg Teachout, Diane Wakoski, her poetry group and each one of her friends for their marvelous feedback and encouragement. She hopes to continue a life of writing and traveling.

Dana Diehl is currently a senior Creative Writing major at Susquehanna University. Next year, she hopes to pursue an MFA in fiction in some new, exciting corner of the country. She lives next to a river and enjoys Amish farmers markets and climbing mountains.

Alexandra Hay hails from Long Island, New York and has been an avid photographer since spending most of her freshman year of high school in a darkroom. She loves to travel and explore the cities of the world, taking photos of urban architecture and cityscapes. Alexandra currently studies English, Russian, and architecture at Princeton University and plans to pursue a career in architecture.

Julia Howland-Myers is a junior Dramatic Arts major, Arabic minor, and Creative Writing minor at the University of North Carolina at Chapel Hill. She's been writing since she can remember, especially during her summers from 2003-2008 at Duke Young Writers' Camp. Within UNC's Creative Writing program, she's been fortunate enough to study with professors Pam Durban and Daniel Wallace. For the moment, she's primarily interested in writing short fiction and short-short fiction. When she's not writing, she's probably acting, producing theatre with her student-run company the LAB! Theatre, drinking coffee, or playing with dogs.

Leena Joshi is a Portland, Oregon native and recent graduate of the University of Washington. She enjoys trees, punk rock, and good food.

Charissa Kim is from Southern California and is currently a freshman studying Communications at University of Illinois in Urbana-Champaign. From a young age, she has been passionate about art, literature, history, and traveling. She hopes to pursue a future career involving public relations or graphic design.

Shira Golden Kresch is a second year student at MSU studying in the Residential College for Arts and Humanities and Studio Art. Her favorite thing about painting is the process. "A lot of times I'll have to use several layers of paint before I'm happy with it, but I think revision is an important part of the experience of art-making or in any creative process," says Kresch. She often chooses portraiture as subject matter because it is a strong way to convey emotion through an image.

Keith Magnuson is an undergraduate student in creative writing at Western Michigan University. He plans on continuing his education at the postgraduate level. He lives in Kalamazoo, MI.

Chase O'Black is a junior at MSU majoring in marketing with a passion for photography. Along with work for the Red Cedar Log yearbook, Chase's photos can be found in Michigan State University's fashion magazine, VIM. Chase's interests include listening to hip-hop music, longboarding, and traveling the world. In the future you might catch him using his creativity to expand his appeal and the minds of everyone around him.

Margaret O'Brien is a senior at Alma College, Alma, MI, where she majors in English Literature and minors in Writing. Prior to transferring to Alma in 2009, she studied English Literature and Medieval History at the University of St Andrews in Scotland. After graduating from Alma, Margaret plans to pursue an MFA and Ph.D. in English Literature and Creative Writing.

Andrew Phillips' life goals are to own a pet sloth and sleep in a hammock pitched between two avocado trees.

Corrine Pratt is very excited to be part of The Red Cedar Review's 47th issue. She is currently an English major at Michigan State University, and hopes to become a secondary education teacher.

Lynette Score was born in the mining town of Harlan, Kentucky and moved to Michigan at the age of six. She is an aspiring National Park Ranger and a Christian. She currently lives in East Lansing with two friends from church and her beloved tortoise, Camille.

Jared Shaffer is an undergraduate student at the University of North Carolina who owes so much to Ben, Jeanne, Jeremy and Will. When asked in a fictitious interview what he would like readers to gain from his stories Jared replied, "I want them to read them and be happier than a dog riding in the back of a pickup truck."

Carrie Walker is a senior writing major at Southeast Missouri State University in Cape Girardeau. She enjoys post-modern and experimental fiction. She currently works in retail, but hopes to find a job in publishing after graduation

Erik James Wilbur feels most at home in Sacramento, California's midtown district. But in 2009, he met his wife and, making an uncharacteristically impulsive decision, moved away from there to be with her. He is currently studying English as an undergraduate at San Diego State University. He has inherited a love of the outdoors from his father, and takes every opportunity to head up into the Sierra Nevada to channel the ghost of John Muir. An archer, fisherman, and bicycle enthusiast, he has also been known to shamelessly spend an entire day in his cluttered studio apartment watching documentaries, or Aaron Sorkin teledramas. After he graduates, he plans to pursue an MFA in creative writing.

Alora Wilde born in Rochester, Michigan in 1989, Alora Wilde has always engaged in creative expression through fine arts. After moving to Missouri in 2005, her artistic explorations were nurtured by high school teachers. In 2007 she continued to St. Louis Community College, refining technical skills and studying formal aspects of art. Transferring to Kansas City Art Institute in 2009 allowed her to cultivate her aesthetic and participate in a larger dialogue. Prior to her first solo exhibition in July 2011, Alora will receive her B.F.A. from KCAI in May of 2012.

Anna Wildfong is a student studying arts and humanities as well as creative writing at Michigan State University.

LIBRARY RECOMMENDATION
FORM *for the* *redcedar*
REVIEW

I'd like to recommend the acquisition of Red Cedar Review (ISSN 0034-1967), published one (1) time per year by Michigan State University Press. Subscription price for U.S. institutions: $36 for 1 year. Price for international intstitutions: $46 for 1 year.

Thank you for your consideration of this request.

_____
SIGNATURE

_____
PRINT NAME

_____
E-MAIL ADDRESS

_____
INSTITUTION

_____
DEPARTMENT

SUBMIT ORDERS TO: Michigan Sate University Press Journals: PO Box 121; Congers, NY 10920-0121; TEL (845) 267-3054; FAX (845) 267-3478; EMAIL msupjournals@cambeywest.com.

Copy, complete, and submit this form to the appropriate collection specialist at your library.

SUBSCRIPTION/RENEWAL
FORM *for the* *redcedar*
REVIEW

1 YEAR

U.S. Individual..........................$18
International Individual...........$28
U.S. Institution.........................$36
International Institution...........$46
Student.....................................$11

Via USPS. *Shipping and handling for each copy: DOMESTIC: $6.00; INTERNATIONAL: $8.00
For airmail, contact *msupjournals@cambeywest.com* for quote before ordering

☐ Yes! I would like to subscribe to *Red Cedar Review.*
☐ Please renew my subscription.

_____
NAME

_____
STREET ADDRESS

_____
CITY / STATE / ZIP

_____
PHONE   FAX

_____
EMAIL (REQUIRED)

☐ Check enclosed, made payable to *Michigan State University Press*
   (All amounts must be in U.S. funds drawn on a U.S. bank.)
☐ Please charge my: ☐ Visa   ☐   MasterCard

_____
PHONE

_____
EMAIL (REQUIRED)

SUBMIT ORDERS TO: Michigan State University Press Journals; PO Box 121;
Congers, NY 10920-0121; TEL (845) 267-3054; FAX (845) 267-3478;
EMAIL *msupjournals@cambeywest.com.*